Grade

6

Name

Date of exam

CW00429223

Contents

Editor for ABRSM: Richard Jones

Other pieces for this grade

First published in 2010 by ABRSM (Publishing) Ltd, a wholly owned subsidiary of ABRSM, 24 Portland Place, London W1B 1LU, United Kingdom

© 2010 by The Associated Board of the Royal Schools of Music

Music origination by Barnes Music Engraving Ltd
Cover by Økvik Design
Printed in England by Headley Brothers Ltd, The Invicta Press, Ashford, Kent

A:1

Almand

First movement from Suite No. 4 in D minor

John Alcock

John Alcock (1715–1806) was an English organist and composer who in 1750 became organist and vicar-choral at Lichfield Cathedral. The *allemande* (of which 'almand' is an English variant) is the first of the four basic movements of the classical dance suite. The short upbeat and flowing semiquavers of this almand are characteristic. Quavers might be lightly detached. Dynamics are left to the player's discretion. The ornament signs have been made more consistent by the editor.

Source: *Six Suite's of Easy Lessons for the Harpsicord or Spinnet* [sic] (London, 1741)

© 1985 by The Associated Board of the Royal Schools of Music
Adapted from Alcock: *Six Suites of Easy Lessons*, edited by Richard Jones (ABRSM)

A:2

Adagio

First movement from Sonata in D, Op. 1 No. 4

Baldassare Galuppi

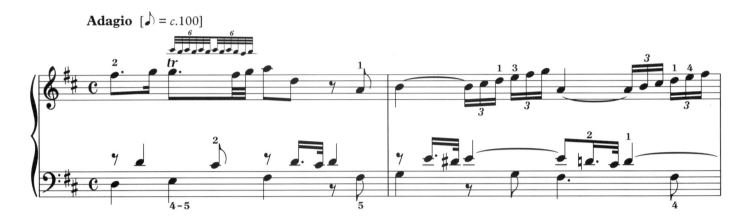

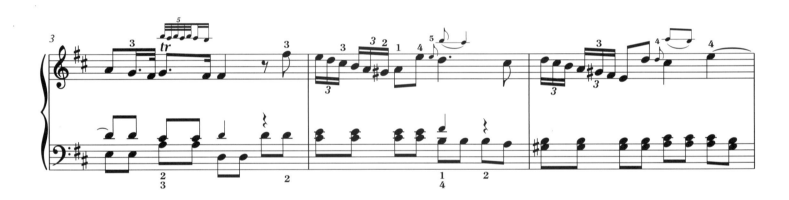

The Italian composer Baldassare Galuppi (1706–85) began his long and successful career as an opera composer in Venice. In 1741–3 he lived in London, presenting operas at the King's Theatre, Haymarket. After his return to Venice he was appointed *vice-maestro*, and later *maestro di cappella*, at St Mark's. He was an important figure in the development of *opera buffa* (comic opera), but he also wrote many serious operas, numerous sacred works and about 130 keyboard sonatas. Dynamics are left to the player's discretion.
Source: *Sonate per cembalo*, Op. 1 (London: Walsh, 1760)

A:3

Allegro

Second movement from Suite in G, HWV 441

G. F. Handel

© 1984 by The Associated Board of the Royal Schools of Music
Adapted from Handel: *Selected Keyboard Works*, Book II, edited by Richard Jones (ABRSM)

Two collections of Handel's keyboard suites were published in London during his lifetime. Whereas the first set (1720) included some of his most recent music for the harpsichord, the second set (c.1733), from which this Allegro is taken, was mostly compiled from music composed at a much earlier period – in many cases, the first decade of the 18th century. In the first five bars of the Allegro and in parallel contexts elsewhere, tenuto touch might be used to build up the broken-chord figuration into full five-part chords. Dynamics are left to the player's discretion.
Source: *Suites de pièces pour le clavecin*, Vol. II (London: Walsh, c.1733)

B:1

Élégie

No. 7 from *Album des enfants*, Series 2, Op. 126

Cécile Chaminade

Cécile Chaminade (1857–1944) was a French pianist and composer who made her debut as a soloist at the age of 18. She was successful as a performer in the early 20th century, touring France, England and the USA where the novelty of a woman playing her own music became a special attraction. Her compositions include not only choral, orchestral and chamber music, and songs, but also about 200 piano pieces, which became popular partly because they were easy enough for amateur pianists.

The pedal indications printed in the source have been omitted here because they might be misleading. However, they do indicate legato pedalling throughout.

Source: *Album des enfants*, 2e série, Op. 126 (Paris: Enoch, 1907)

Reproduced by kind permission of Editions Enoch & Cie
All enquiries about this piece, apart from those directly relating to the exams, should be addressed to United Music Publishers Ltd, 33 Lea Road, Waltham Abbey, Essex EN9 1ES.

Allegro moderato

No. 5 from *Poetic Tone-Pictures*, Op. 3

B:2

Edited by Angus Morrison

Edvard Grieg

The Norwegian composer and pianist Edvard Grieg (1843–1907) was especially adept at writing miniature character-pieces for the piano. Among the earliest of these are the six *Poetic Tone-Pictures*, Op. 3, which were first published in 1864 when the composer was only 21. Angus Morrison points out that many of Grieg's musical fingerprints are already strongly in evidence in this collection, notably the falling leading-notes in No. 5, the piece selected here.
Source: *Poetiske tonebilleder*, Op. 3 (Copenhagen, 1864)

Mignon

No. 4 from Five Piano Pieces, Op. 3

Edited by Alan Jones

Carl Nielsen

Moderato grazioso ♩ = 108

più mosso

The Danish composer Carl Nielsen (1865–1931) studied at the Copenhagen Conservatory from 1884 to 1886 and played the violin in the Danish court orchestra from 1889 to 1905. His early music, including the Op. 3 piano pieces of 1890, from which 'Mignon' is taken, is written in a late Romantic style. 'Mignon' is inscribed 'And she danced, but with painful sorrow in her heart.' This inscription suggests a reference to Goethe's novel *Wilhelm Meister's Apprenticeship*, in which the heroine is called Mignon. An acceptable tempo for this piece in the exam would be ♩ = *c*.96. Source: *Fem klaverstykker*, Op. 3 (Copenhagen, 1891)

Reproduced from *A Romantic Sketchbook for Piano*, Book IV, edited by Alan Jones (ABRSM)

Soirée Polka

Stephen C. Foster

The American composer Stephen C. Foster (1826–64) was largely self-taught as a musician. He became the most popular American songwriter of his day, composing some 200 songs in the 20-year period 1844–64, but he nonetheless died in poverty and obscurity. The polka is a Bohemian dance that originated around 1830 and soon became fashionable throughout Europe and America. Foster's *Soirée Polka* dates from 1850.

The LH D in b. 3 is given as B in the source but has been changed in this edition by analogy with b. 43. The RH slurs in bb. 49, 50, 53 and 54 are longer in the source, lasting for the whole bar; they have been shortened here by analogy with the equivalent section starting at b. 9.

Source: *Soirée Polka* (Baltimore: W. C. Peters, 1850)

à Mademoiselle Berthe Duranton

Pastoral

C:2

Joaquín Rodrigo

The Spanish composer Joaquín Rodrigo (1901–99), who was blind from infancy, studied with Paul Dukas at the École Normale in Paris from 1927. After further studies at the Sorbonne in the 1930s, he finally returned to Spain in 1939. In 1947 he was appointed to the Manuel de Falla Chair of Music at the University of Madrid, a professorship created for him that he held for 30 years. His most famous work, the *Concierto de Aranjuez* for guitar and orchestra, was premiered in 1940. Although Rodrigo was inspired by elements of Iberian culture – musical, literary and historical – he developed his own sonorities to form a melodious and colourful style.

  Pastoral is an early work, dating from 1926. According to the composer, it was 'written in terms of the 18th-century eclogue' (a type of pastoral poem) and 'inspired more or less by springtime', hence the cuckoo in bb. 37–43. The dissonant B♯ adds colour to the pause chord in b. 70.
Source: *Pastoral pour piano* (Paris: Eschig, 1936)

© 1992 by Ediciones Joaquín Rodrigo, S. A.
All enquiries about this piece, apart from those directly relating to the exams, should be addressed to Ediciones Joaquín Rodrigo, General Yagüe 11–4° J, 28020 Madrid, Spain.

Clouds

No. 2 from *Piano Pieces for Children*

Tōru Takemitsu

The Japanese composer Tōru Takemitsu (1930–96) was largely self-taught. Among the chief influences on his musical style were the French composers Debussy and Messiaen. His collection *Piano Pieces for Children*, from which 'Clouds' is taken, was first published in 1979.